ATTAINMENT'S

Right On Reader 1

Pamela J. Mims • Angel Lee • Tracie-Lynn Zakas • Diane M. Browder

Right On Reader 1

Pamela J. Mims
Angel Lee
Tracie-Lynn Zakas
Diane M. Browder

Graphic design: Elizabeth Ragsdale & Sherry Pribbenow
Illustration: Jo Reynolds & Beverly Potts
Editing: Linda R. Schreiber

An Attainment Company Publication

Printed in the United States of America
ISBN: 1-57861-841-X

Attainment Company, Inc.

P.O. Box 930160 • Verona, Wisconsin 53593-0160 USA
Phone: 800-327-4269 • Fax: 800.942.3865
www.AttainmentCompany.com

Contents

UNIT ONE

UNIT TWO

UNIT ONE

Change

Holes

By Louis Sachar

Based on the book *Holes,* by Louis Sachar.

CONTENTS

CHAPTER

CHAPTER 1

Camp Green Lake

 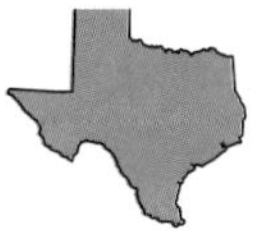 

The largest lake in Texas used to be Green Lake. Now Green

Lake is dry. The water has gone and the land is flat and

dry. The people of the town moved away when the lake went

 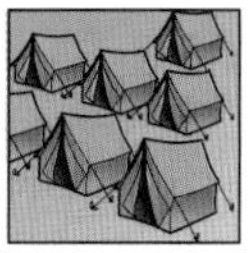 

dry. But Camp Green Lake is still there. Camp Green Lake is a

camp for boys who have made bad decisions. Each boy has to

  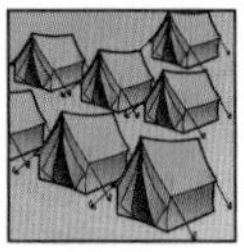

dig a hole every day at this camp.

At Camp Green Lake, boys dug holes.

Stanley Yelnats was not really a bad boy, but a judge said

  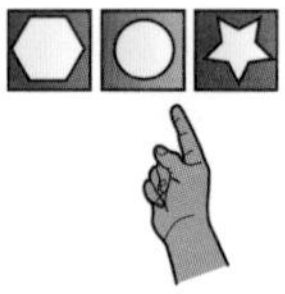

he was guilty anyway. The judge gave Stanley a choice. Stanley

could go to jail or to Camp Green Lake. The judge did not

tell Stanley what the camp was. Stanley's family was poor and

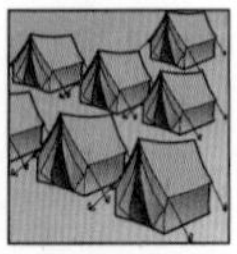  

he had never been to camp. He thought camp would be fun.

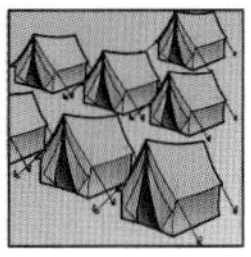 

He picked Camp Green Lake. Stanley had a lot of trouble in

his life. He blamed his trouble on his great-great-grandfather.

  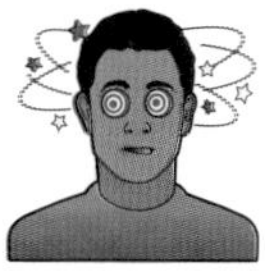 

Stanley's family said that a gypsy put a curse on Stanley's

great-great-grandfather because he broke a promise.

 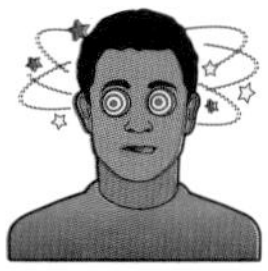

Stanley thought the curse was why he had to go to

Camp Green Lake.

At Camp Green Lake, boys dug holes.

CHAPTER 2

This Camp Is Not Fun

Stanley got off the bus at Camp Green Lake. Camp Green Lake

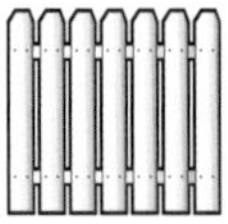  

had no fences but the warden did not have to worry about

boys running away. There was nowhere to run. Stanley was

assigned to Tent D. In Tent D, he met the other boys. The

boys told Stanley he would have to dig a big hole! Every day!

At Camp Green Lake, boys dug holes.

 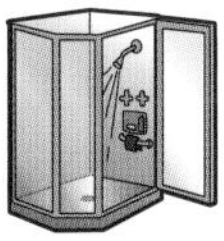 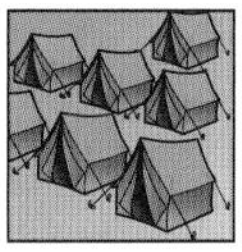

Stanley took a shower. Water was scarce at Camp Green Lake

so his shower was short. Next, Stanley ate dinner. The boys

asked Stanley why he was sent to Camp Green Lake. Stanley

told them the judge found him guilty of stealing a pair of

 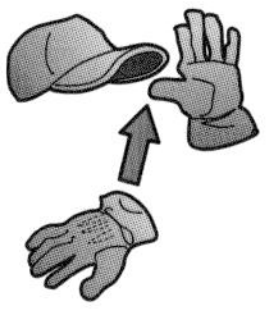 

sneakers. The sneakers belonged to a famous basketball player.

Stanley told the boys how it happened. He was walking home

one day. The sneakers fell from a bridge. One sneaker hit

 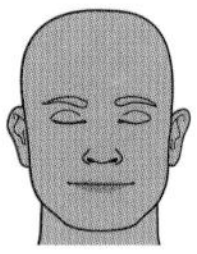 

Stanley in the head. It turned out the sneakers had been

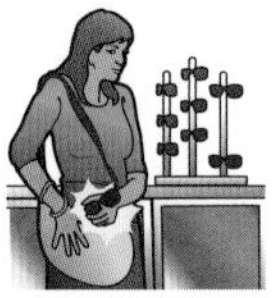   

stolen from a homeless shelter. The police saw Stanley with the

   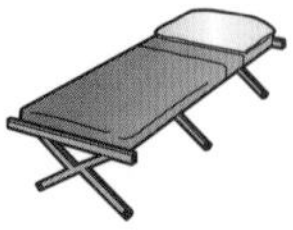

sneakers and arrested him. After dinner, Stanley laid on his cot.

He tried to sleep. In the morning, the boys started digging

holes in the dry lake. Stanley dug his first hole and got a

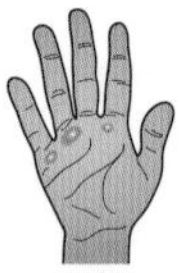  

lot of blisters on his hands. Camp Green Lake was not a fun

place. Digging was hard work. It was very hot. Stanley was

 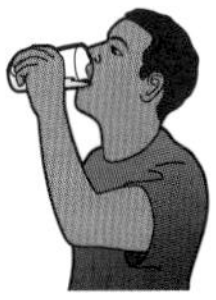 

so thirsty. He wanted a drink of water. He wanted to take a

shower. Finally, the boys finished digging and returned to camp.

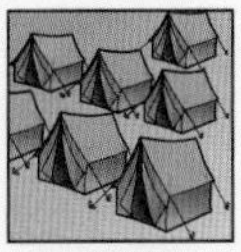 

At Camp Green Lake, boys dug holes.

  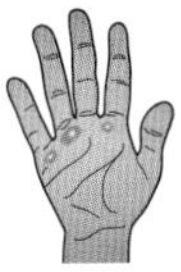 

Stanley was tired. His blisters on his hands hurt! He missed his

family. Before Stanley went to sleep, he wrote a letter to his

family. He didn't tell them that Camp Green Lake was not fun.

CHAPTER 3

Stanley Wants a Day Off

The next day, Stanley's body hurt. It even hurt to lift his

spoon to eat breakfast. Stanley started digging his second hole.

He found a rock with fish fossils in it. Stanley remembered

the day off rule. When someone found a treasure the warden

liked, that person could get the day off. He hoped the warden

liked this treasure. Stanley showed it to his camp counselor,

Mr. Pendanski. Mr. Pendanski said the fossil was not a treasure.

Stanley had to keep working.

Stanley found a treasure.

  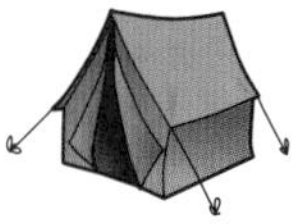 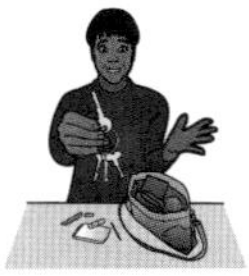

X-Ray was the leader of Tent D. After Stanley found the

treasure, X-ray asked Stanley to give him the next interesting

thing he found. Stanley wanted the boys to like him. He said

OK to X-Ray. Stanley was the last one to finish digging his

 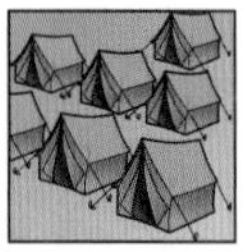 

hole again. When he got back to camp, Mr. Pendanski was

talking with all of the boys. He wanted the boys to start

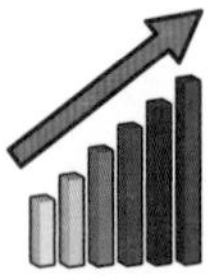  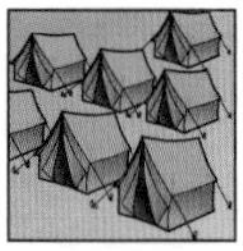

making goals for when they left the camp. He wanted them to

know they were in charge of their futures. All the boys had

nicknames. They named Stanley "the Caveman." He was glad they

gave him a nickname. It meant the boys liked him.

Stanley found a treasure.

The next day, Stanley started digging his 14th hole. After

lunch, he found something shiny in the dirt in his hole.

  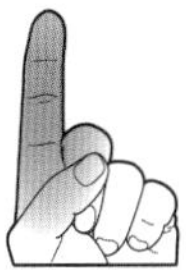

It was a narrow gold tube about the size of his index finger.

It had a heart with the letters K. B. carved in it. Stanley didn't

think Mr. Pendanski would think it was a treasure so he gave

it to X-Ray.

CHAPTER 4

Zero Wants to Learn to Read

Early the next day, X-Ray showed the treasure to Mr. Pendanski.

If the warden liked it, X-Ray could get most of the day off.

Mr. Pendanski showed the gold tube to the warden. The warden

liked the treasure a lot. X-Ray got the day off. He got extra

time in the shower. He got clean clothes, too.

Stanley found a treasure.

 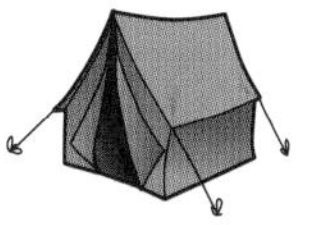

All the boys from Tent D got special treatment. They got extra

water in their canteens. After this, X-Ray was nicer to Stanley.

The other boys were nicer to Stanley, too. The warden wanted

the boys to keep looking for treasures. She made them look

through loose piles of dirt. They looked in the dirt near X-Ray's

hole. The warden stayed with them all day. She wanted to

make sure no treasures were missed. The warden told the

 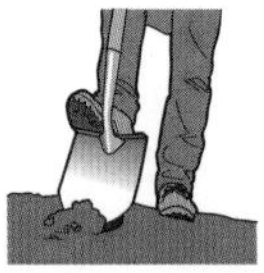 

boys to dig faster. The boys dug in pairs. That was easier

than digging alone. Stanley knew they were all digging in

the wrong place.

Stanley found a treasure.

   **3**

The boys kept digging the same holes. The three holes were so

big, they became one giant hole. Tent D boys dug longer than

the others boys at Camp Green Lake. While digging, Stanley got

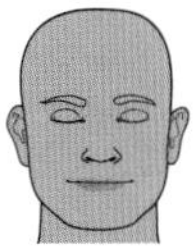   

hit in the head with a shovel. Mr. Pendanski and the warden

made him keep working. The warden gave up. The boys had

not found any new treasures. Each boy went back to digging

  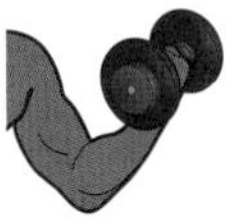

his own hole again. Stanley had gotten much stronger. He was

 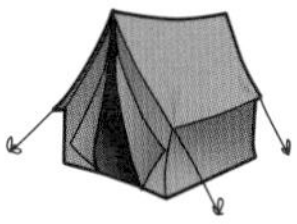  

still the slowest. Back at Tent D, Stanley got a letter from his

mom. Stanley wrote a letter back to her. He wanted his mom

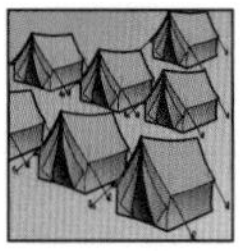  

to think Camp Green Lake was a lot of fun. He told his mom

he was learning how to swim and making lots of friends.

Zero saw Stanley writing a letter. Zero asked Stanley to teach

him how to read.

Stanley found a treasure.

CHAPTER 5

Stanley Needs a Friend

  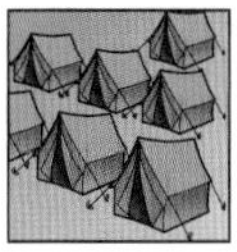

Mr. Sir drove the water truck at the camp. He loved to

eat sunflower seeds. One day, Magnet took Mr. Sir's bag of

sunflower seeds from the water truck. When the boys were

  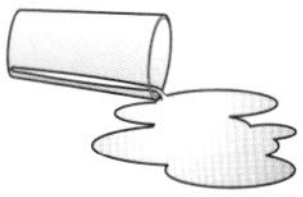 

eating the seeds, the bag accidentally spilled in Stanley's hole.

When Mr. Sir discovered his seeds were gone, he knew the

 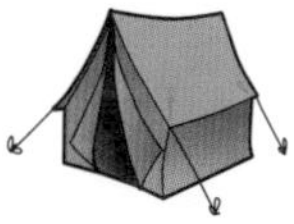

boys from Tent D took them. He wanted them back right

  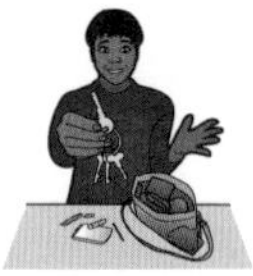

away. Mr. Sir looked for the seeds. He found the whole bag in

   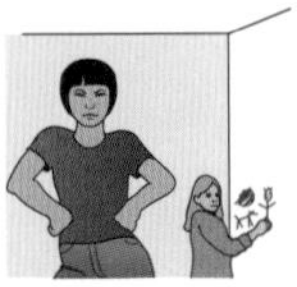

Stanley's hole. Mr. Sir was very mad. Stanley was in big trouble.

Mr. Sir took Stanley to see the warden. But the warden got

mad at Mr. Sir for bringing Stanley to her cabin. The warden

had special nail polish. It had snake venom in it. It was

  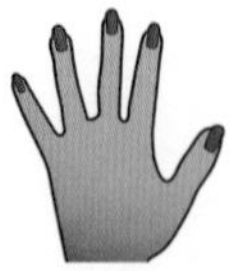

poisonous when wet. She painted some on her fingernails. Then

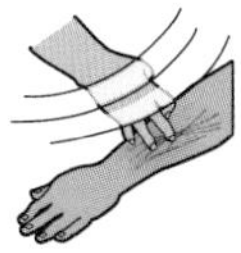   

she scratched Mr. Sir with her wet fingernails. The snake venom

made Mr. Sir very sick. Stanley was sent back to his hole. He

  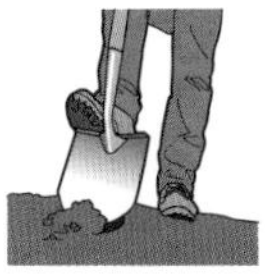 

was surprised to see his hole was dug. He thanked all the

boys. Stanley did not steal the sunflower seeds but he took the

blame for it. The boys were thankful. But then he saw that

Zero had the most left to dig in his hole. He knew that Zero

had dug the hole for him.

Stanley and Zero became friends.

Stanley asked Zero why he helped him. Zero said he knew

Stanley did not steal the sunflower seeds, or the sneakers!

Zero knew that Stanley was not a bad boy. Zero knew

Stanley needed a friend.

Stanley and Zero became friends.

Zero wanted to know how to read. Stanley wanted to do

something nice for Zero. Stanley decided to teach Zero to read.

He taught Zero how to write his name. That night, Stanley was

in his bed. He thought about the gold tube he had found.

He remembered seeing something like it before. His mother had

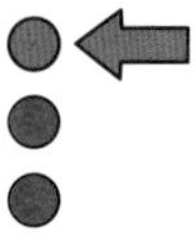  

one like it. It was the top of a lipstick tube. This tube had

the letters K.B. on it. Maybe the letters meant something.

Stanley and Zero became friends.

CHAPTER 6

Kate Barlow Loves the Onion Man

In the past, Green Lake had been a beautiful place to live.

Every year on the 4th of July, the people from Green Lake

would picnic around the lake. Kate Barlow was the only teacher

in Green Lake. She taught everyone in the town to read. She

taught the children to read during the day. She taught the

men to read in the evening. She also made the best spiced

peaches in town. Trout Walker was the richest man in town.

He liked Kate a lot. He wanted to take her for a ride in his

new boat. Kate said, "No thank you." Trout got mad. Sam, the

Onion Man, sold onions. He believed that onions were the secret

to a long and healthy life. When the people of Green Lake

were sick, they got better when they ate Sam's onions. One

day, Kate asked Sam to repair the schoolhouse. She paid Sam

with her delicious spiced peaches. Sam made the schoolhouse

look brand-new. That made Kate happy so she taught Sam

to read. Sam and Kate fell in love. This was a big problem

because Sam was a black man and Kate was a white woman.

Kate loved Sam, the Onion Man.

One day, they kissed each other in the middle of town. It was

against the law for a black man to kiss a white woman. Sam

 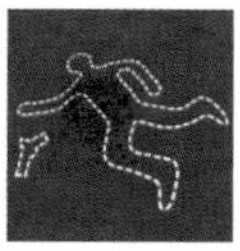

would have to be punished. He would have to be killed.

Kate loved Sam, the Onion Man.

To punish Kate, Trout Walker and other men burned the

schoolhouse. Kate was mad. She wanted to be with Sam. They

tried to run away together on Sam's boat. Trout's boat was

faster and caught up to them. The town's people killed Sam.

Kate Barlow killed the sheriff and ran away. She was gone

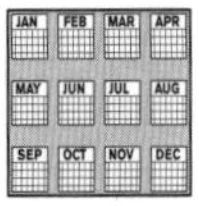

for 20 years.

Kate loved Sam, the Onion Man.

Kate became an outlaw. She robbed banks. She even robbed

Stanley's great-great-grandfather. When she returned to Green Lake,

the water in the lake was all gone. The lake was dry. It had

not rained for 20 years. She found a cabin and buried her

treasure. Her treasure was the money she had stolen from the

banks. One day, Trout found Kate. He wanted her treasure. Kate

would not give it to him. Then a yellow-spotted lizard bit her

and she died.

Kate loved Sam, the Onion Man.

CHAPTER 7

Stanley and Zero Make a Deal

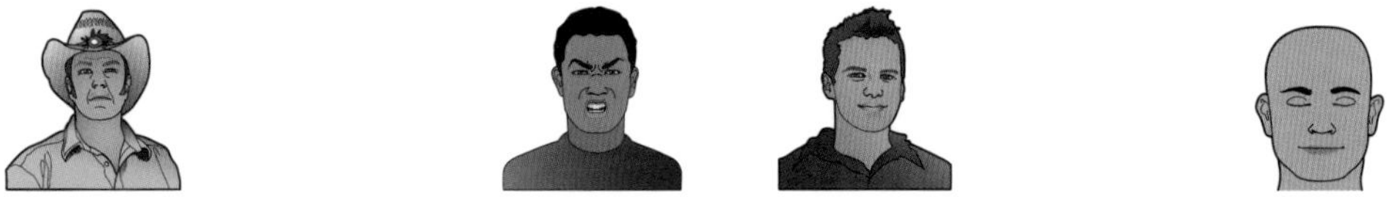

Mr. Sir was very mad at Stanley. Mr. Sir's face was swollen half

the size of a cantaloupe. A boy from a different tent asked

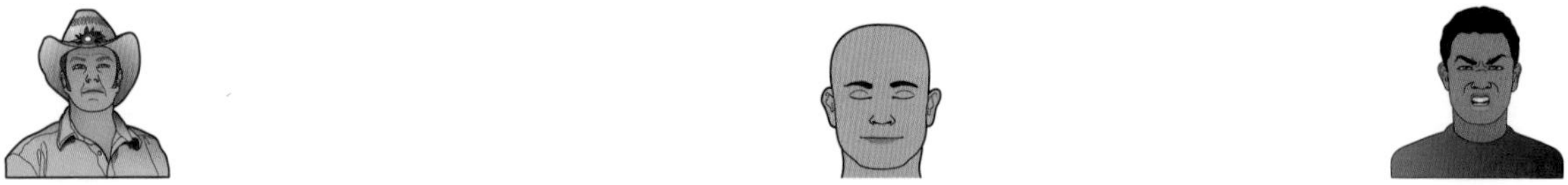

Mr. Sir what happened to his face. Mr. Sir was so mad he

hit the boy. Stanley kept quiet.

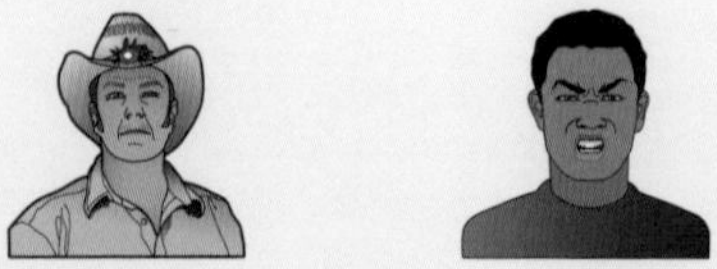

Mr. Sir was mad.

Mr. Sir punished Stanley. He did not refill his water canteen.

Instead of putting the water in the canteen, Mr. Sir poured

it on the ground. The boys decided to help each other.

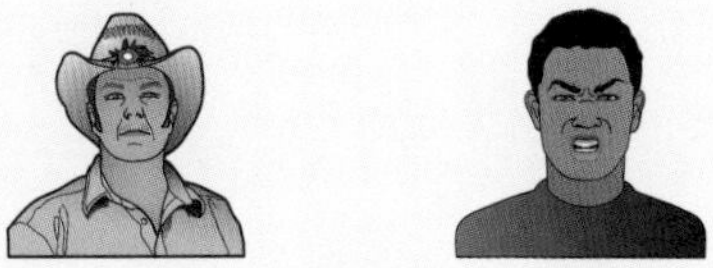

Mr. Sir was mad.

Mr. Sir did not fill Stanley's canteen for many days. Mr.

Pendanski gave Stanley extra water because he knew Stanley was

not getting enough. Stanley learned to drink just a little water

every day. One day, Mr. Sir started filling Stanley's canteen with

water again. That made Stanley suspicious. Stanley was afraid

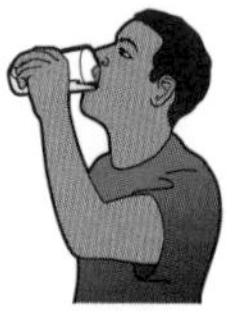

Mr. Sir had put poison in his water so he did not drink it.

Mr. Sir was mad.

When they were not busy digging holes, Stanley taught Zero to

read and write. Zero worked hard to learn to read and write.

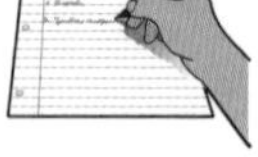

Zero could write all the letters of the alphabet. He could even

write his name. One afternoon, Stanley heard thunder over the

mountains. He hoped it would rain. The lightning lit up the sky

and Stanley saw some rocks on the top of the mountain. The

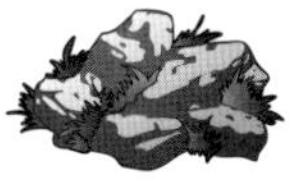 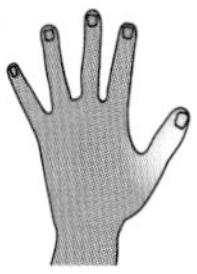 

rocks looked like a fist with a thumb pointing toward the sky.

He remembered a story his great-great-grandfather had told him.

After Kate Barlow robbed him, his great-great-grandfather survived

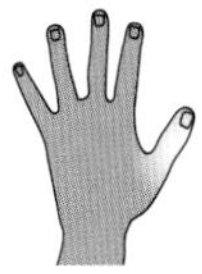  

on "God's Thumb." This was the deal the boys made. Zero

would dig half of Stanley's holes and Stanley would teach Zero

to read. The deal made the other boys mad. Zig Zag was so

mad he picked a fight with Stanley. Stanley was not a good

fighter and was hurt. Mr. Pendanski fired his gun into the air.

Stanley told the adults about the deal. Mr. Pendanski could not

believe Zero could read. He asked Zero how to spell a word.

Zero refused to spell the word and Mr. Pendanski called Zero

stupid. Zero got mad and hit Mr. Pendanski's head with

  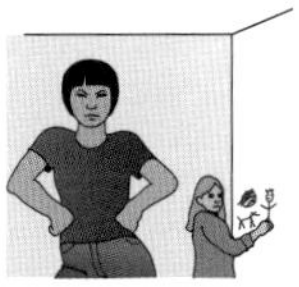 

a shovel. Zero was in big trouble. He took off running.

Mr. Sir was mad.

CHAPTER 8

Stanley and Zero Find "God's Thumb"

Mr. Sir punished Stanley for teaching Zero to read. Stanley had

to dig Zero's holes because Zero had run away. Stanley worried

about Zero. He hoped Zero would make it across the lake to

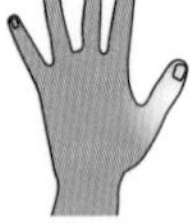  

"God's Thumb." Zero did not come back. The adults thought he

would die. All the information about Zero was destroyed. The

 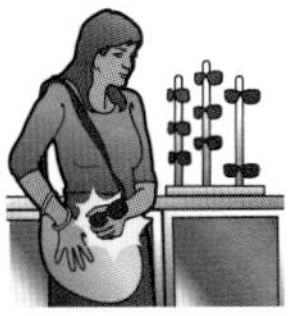  

next day Stanley tried to steal the water truck to save his

 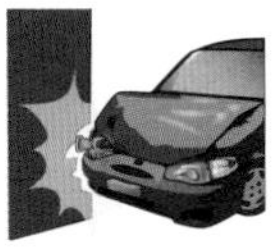 

friend. He accidentally drove it into a hole.

Stanley helped his friend.

Stanley took off running. Nobody came after him. Stanley walked

all day in the hot sun and saw a lot of holes. He had no

water in his canteen. It was empty. Then Stanley saw Zero.

 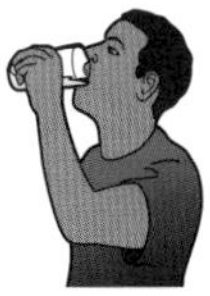  

He was still alive, but Zero needed a drink of water. Stanley

dragged Zero to an upside down boat in the middle of the

dry lake. There they found jars with something sweet in them.

They were very hungry and thirsty.

Stanley helped his friend.

Zero called the fruity contents in the jars sploosh. They drank

  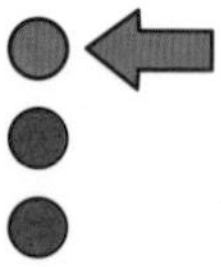

all the sploosh in the boat. Stanley wanted to go the top of

the mountain. The boys walked for a long time. They carried

the shovel, a burlap bag, and jars of sploosh. Zero drank from

the jars that were easy to open. He got very sick from the

sploosh. Stanley had to help Zero. Zero was very weak. The

boys reached a tall cliff. Stanley wanted to stop and rest but

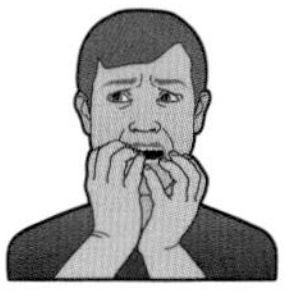  

he was afraid that if Zero stopped, he would not start up

2   

again. The two boys climbed up the tall cliff. Stanley spelled

words for Zero to say back to him. He wanted to keep Zero

from feeling sick. They made it out of the dry lake and

climbed up the side of the mountain.

Stanley helped his friend.

There they saw bugs and weeds. Zero threw up and collapsed.

Stanley carried Zero for a long time. He had to leave the

shovel and burlap bag behind. Stanley was weak, too, and

he tripped and fell. He could not carry Zero anymore. It was

muddy where Stanley fell. He thought to himself that if there

is mud, there must be water. He dug deep and found water.

Stanley and Zero drank the muddy water and fell asleep.

Stanley helped his friend.

CHAPTER 9

Zero Tells the Truth

The boys woke up early the next morning. Both were very

tired. They drank more muddy water. Stanley dug the hole

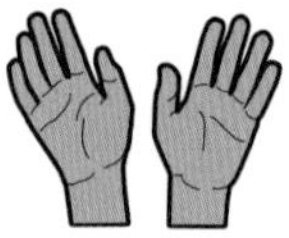  

deeper with his hands. He found an onion. The two friends

shared the onion. They rested for two more days. They ate

onions and drank water. Stanley went back down the mountain

to get the  shovel and  jars in the  burlap bag. Stanley  walked a long way. He could not  believe he  carried Zero that far.

The  friends lived on the  mountain for a week. Before  Camp Green Lake,  Zero lived in a  homeless shelter. He needed a pair of shoes and he saw  sneakers at the  homeless shelter. No one was using the  sneakers so he 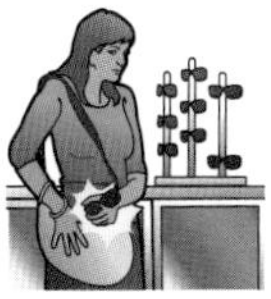 took them.  Zero did not know they 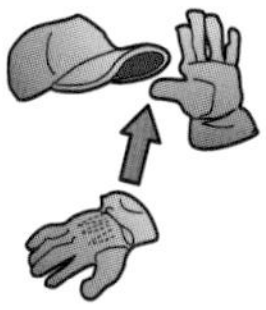 belonged to someone famous.

Zero told the truth.

Zero told Stanley that he stole the sneakers. No one at the

homeless shelter noticed the sneakers on Zero's feet. When

he learned the sneakers were famous, he ran away from the

  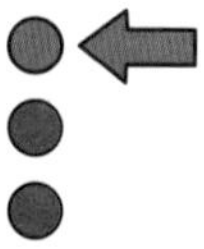

homeless shelter. Zero took them off and left them on top of

a car. A few days later, Zero was arrested for stealing a brand

new pair of sneakers from a store.

Zero told the truth.

 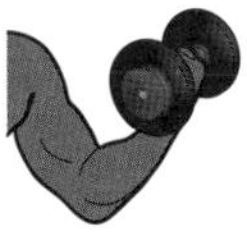  

The boys got stronger. They realized that if Zero had not stolen

the sneakers from the shelter, they would not have become

 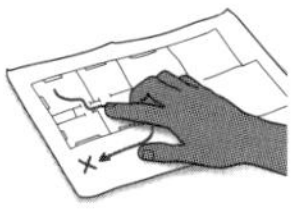

friends. Stanley knew it was destiny. They made a plan to

return to camp. Stanley kept thinking about the gold tube.

Zero told the truth.

CHAPTER 10

Stanley Finds the Treasure

They made it back to 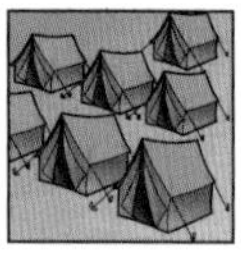 camp in one 

day. They  waited until everyone was  sleeping. They started  digging in the  hole where  Stanley found the  gold tube. It was  dark outside. He could not  see his 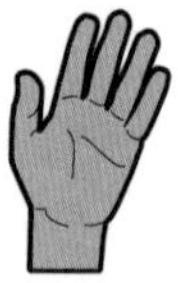 hand in front of his 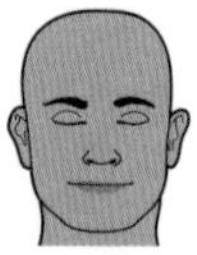 face. Stanley  dug until he hit something hard. It was a metal  box. He kept  digging until

the metal box was free.

Stanley found the real treasure.

Suddenly, a bright light shone on Stanley's face. It was the

warden. Stanley gave the box to Zero to hold. Stanley was

blinded by the light. He did not see the yellow-spotted

lizards on Zero. He did not know they were in a nest

of poisonous lizards.

Mr. Pendanski, Mr. Sir, and all the other adults arrived at

the hole. They were afraid of the lizards. They thought one might attack.

Stanley found the real treasure.

The adults tried to make a plan. The sun came up and the

lizards crawled back into the shaded hole. Zero read the name

on the box—Stanley Yelnats. The treasure belonged to Stanley.

It was his great-great-grandfather's. Stanley's lawyer arrived at

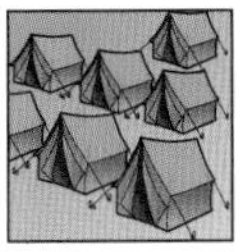 

Camp Green Lake. Stanley was freed. His lawyer discovered that

  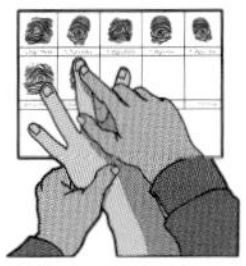

Stanley was innocent. Zero was freed, too, because his records

had been destroyed when he ran away. At last, Stanley and

 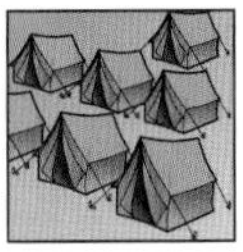 

Zero could leave Camp Green Lake. They rode away in the

lawyer's air-conditioned car. The lawyer made them keep the

back windows open because they smelled like onions. It turned

out that lizards hate the smell of onions. Because Stanley and

Zero had eaten a lot of onions, the lizards stayed away from

them. Eating the onions had kept them safe.

Stanley found the real treasure.

We Beat the Street

By Drs. Sampson Davis, George Jenkins, and Rameck Hunt

Based on the book *We Beat the Streets,* by the Three Doctors: Drs. Sampson Davis, George Jenkins, and Rameck Hunt.

CONTENTS

CHAPTER

CHAPTER 1

Life in the Projects

Life in the ghetto of Newark, New Jersey, was tough, especially

   3

for kids. Sampson, Rameck, and George were three black kids

  6 

who lived in the projects. Sampson was six and loved to play

with his friends and his brother. One summer day, Sampson was

playing with his brother and friends in the park. He hurt his

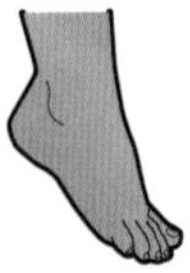 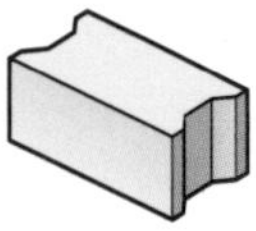 

foot when a cement slab fell on it. Sampson had to go to

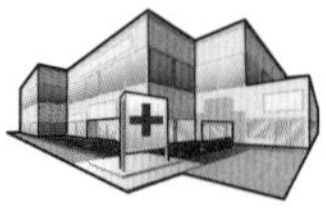 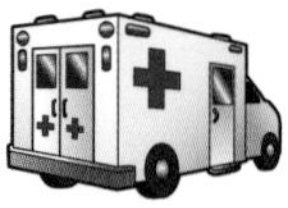

the hospital. He was fascinated with the emergency room. He

asked the doctor lots of questions.

Life in the projects was tough.

Rameck was nine and he loved to learn. But schoolwork was

too easy for him and he was bored. His mother sent him to

a Catholic school so he could get a good education. Rameck

got into a lot of fights. The nuns wanted to put him in

special education. In the public school he went to, he was

in a gifted program.

Life in the projects was tough.

George was eight and loved school. He didn't tell the other

kids in his neighborhood because he didn't want to be different.

His teacher even told him he could go to college. When

George got braces on his teeth, he fell in love with dentistry.

All three boys came from rough neighborhoods. They were

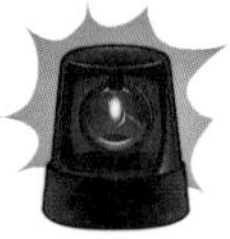  

used to the sounds of sirens. Drug dealers hung on the street

corners. People got into fights and were killed all the time. But

they were smart boys who wanted to be different from others

in their neighborhood. They knew it would be very difficult.

Life in the projects was tough.

CHAPTER 2

Having Goals Isn't Easy

Sampson, George, and Rameck met at University High School.

It was a special school for kids who wanted to go to college.

They became good friends. They understood each other because

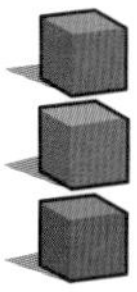

they came from similar backgrounds. It was hard for them to

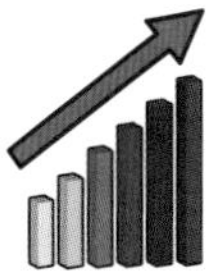 

have goals because they lived in bad neighborhoods. Some of

the others from their neighborhoods dropped out of school, sold

drugs, or even got shot.

Having goals wasn't easy.

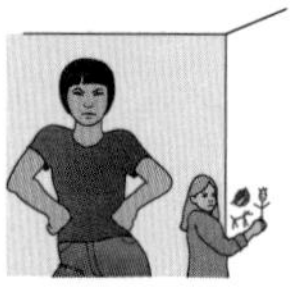

Sometimes they got into trouble, too. They tried to do the

right thing, but it wasn't always easy. Sampson even got

 **2**  

arrested two times. He was lucky though and got out of jail.

  **3** 

Rameck got arrested three times and he also got out of jail.

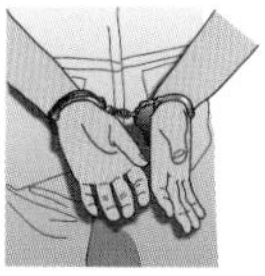 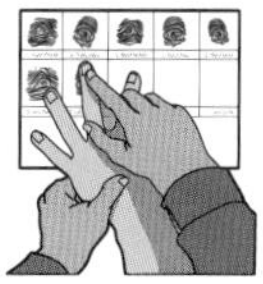 

The arrests did not go on a criminal record thankfully. Rameck

wanted to make a difference. He wanted black people to be

respected. George wanted to go to college.

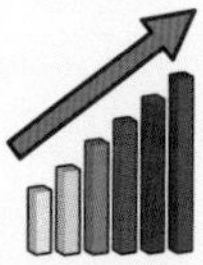

Having goals wasn't easy.

The boys learned they could go to Seton Hall College for free.

They decided to try it. They filled out the application and went

for an interview. All three were accepted. The friends made a

  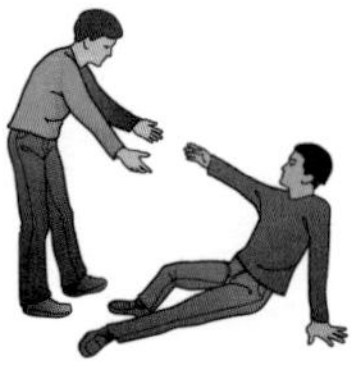

pact. They would go to college together and help each other.

They would be different from others in their neighborhood.

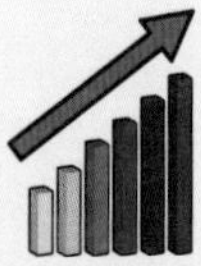

Having goals wasn't easy.

CHAPTER 3

Three Friends Make a Pact

Sampson, Rameck, and George graduated from high school. They

  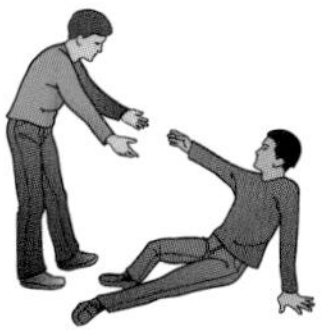

went into a summer program at Seton Hall College that helped

prepare them for college classes in the fall. Their life at college

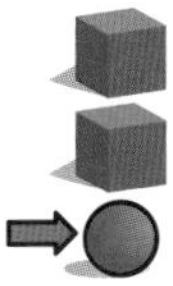 

was very different from their life in their neighborhood. They

 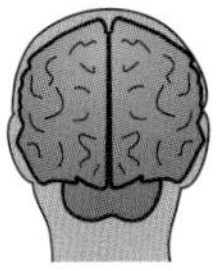

loved the new experience. Their minds were being challenged.

They finished the summer program.

3  

The three friends honored their pact.

In the fall, they started college. They thought they were ready.

They lived in the same dorm. They talked to and supported

each other. They met a teacher at the college who was

determined to see them finish.

3  

The three friends honored their pact.

?

Still, life was not easy for them. They each had questions about

themselves. They had to fight other temptations. College was

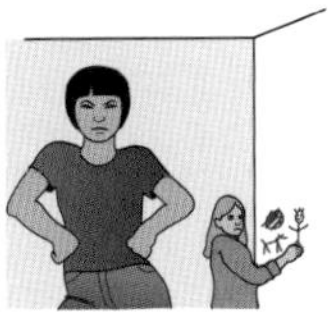

hard work. They still got into trouble sometimes, especially when

 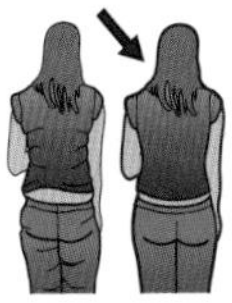

they went home. Now, they didn't feel like they fit in their old

 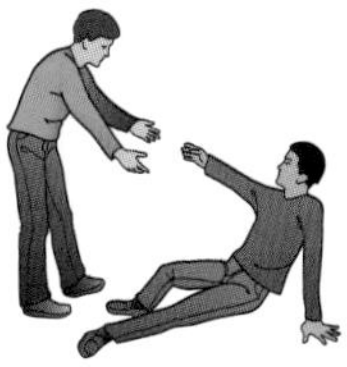

neighborhoods. The decided they wanted to help kids from the

projects know about college. They started a club called Ujima.

3  

The three friends honored their pact.

CHAPTER 4

The Three Friends Finish

Sampson, Rameck, and George were separated during their last

year of college, but they still had a strong friendship. Rameck

and Sampson went to medical school. George went to dental

school. Sampson was afraid medical school was too hard for

him. His friends encouraged him to go. Then he failed his

medical school test. He thought this was a sign.

They couldn't believe they did it!

Sampson studied hard and took the test again. This time he

passed it. Then it was time for the friends to work on their

  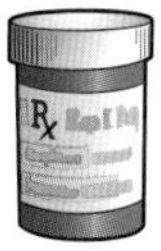

medical rotations. Rameck wanted to work in internal medicine.

 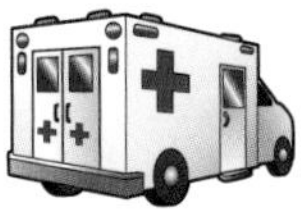

Sampson wanted to work in the emergency room. Finally,

 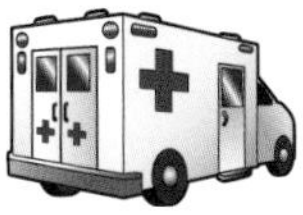 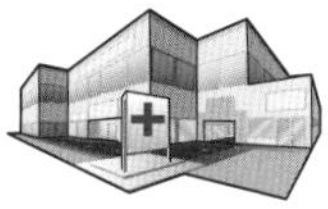

Sampson got a job in the emergency room at the hospital

in his old neighborhood. He would finally get to go home.

They couldn't believe they did it!

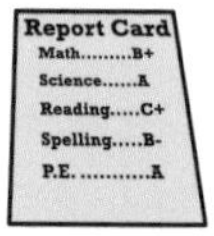

All of the friends finished their education. Sampson and Rameck

became doctors. George became a dentist. They had worked hard

to reach their dreams. They wanted to quit many times, but

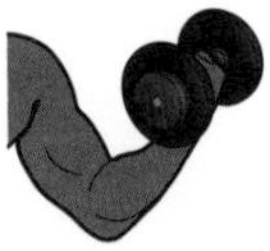

they always had each other. This strong friendship helped them

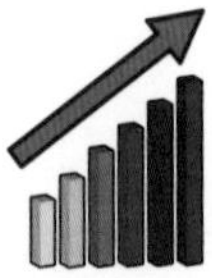

reach their goals, but it wasn't easy.

They couldn't believe they did it!

Still I Rise

By Maya Angelou

Adapted from the poem "Still I Rise," by Maya Angelou. From the *And Still I Rise Poem Collection,* ©1978 by Maya Angelou. Reprinted with permission of Random House.

You may write me down in history

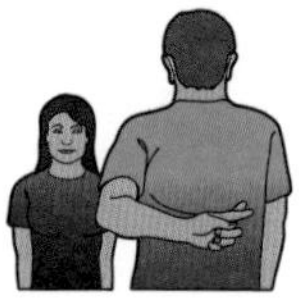

With your bitter, twisted lies,

You may trod me in the very dirt

But still, like dust, I'll rise.

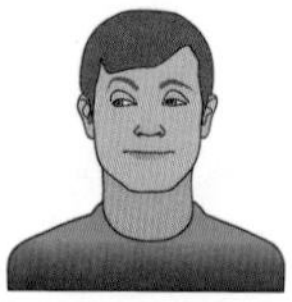

Does my sassiness upset you?

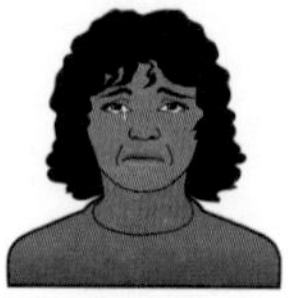

Why are you beset with gloom?

'Cause I walk like I've got oil wells

Pumping in my living room.

Just like moons and like suns,

With the certainty of tides,

Just like hopes springing high,

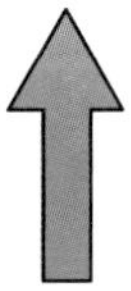

Still I'll rise.

Did you want to see me broken?

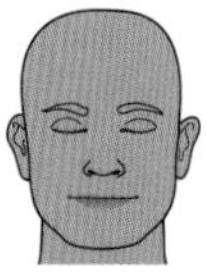 

Bowed head and lowered eyes?

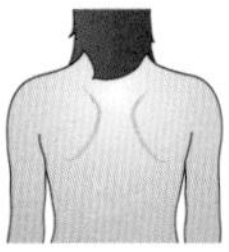 

Shoulders falling down like teardrops.

Weakened by my soulful cries.

Does my haughtiness offend you?

Don't you take it awful hard

'Cause I laugh like I've got gold mines

Diggin' in my own backyard.

You may shoot me with your words,

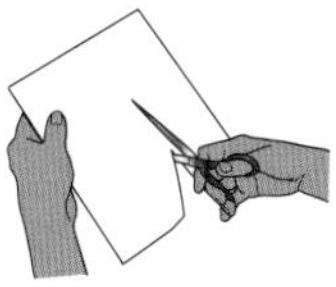 

You may cut me with your eyes,

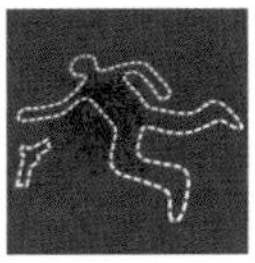 

You may kill me with your hatefulness,

But still, like air, I'll rise.

Does my sexiness upset you?

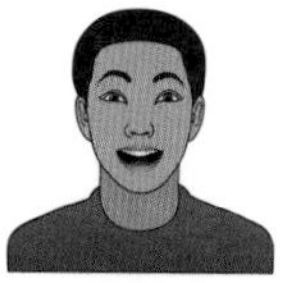

Does it come as a surprise

 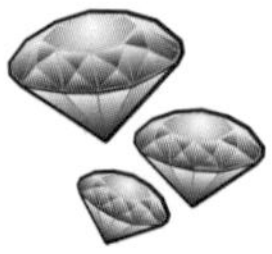

That I dance like I've got diamonds

At the meeting of my thighs?

Out of the huts of history's shame

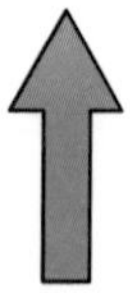

I rise

Up from a past that's rooted in pain

I rise

I'm a black ocean, leaping and wide,

Welling and swelling I bear in the tide.

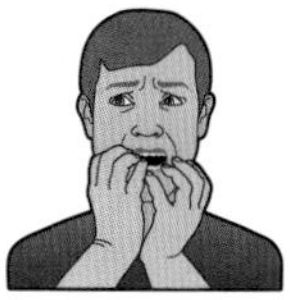

Leaving behind nights of terror and fear

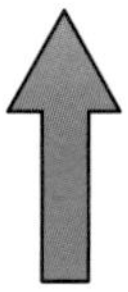

I rise

Into a daybreak that's wondrously clear

I rise

 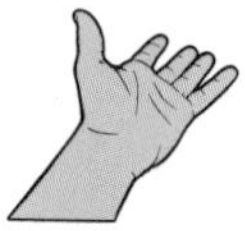

Bringing the gifts that my ancestors gave,

I am the dream and the hope of the slave.

I rise

I rise

I rise.

Changes

A butterfly is an insect.

Before it becomes a butterfly, the insect goes through changes.

2

First an egg is fixed to a leaf. The egg grows for about two

weeks. A caterpillar hatches from the egg.

Before it becomes a butterfly, the insect goes through changes.

Caterpillars are like fuzzy worms. Caterpillars are also called

larvae. The caterpillar will eat many leaves and it will grow.

Before it becomes a butterfly, the insect goes through changes.

Next, the caterpillar attaches itself to a branch or leaf and spins

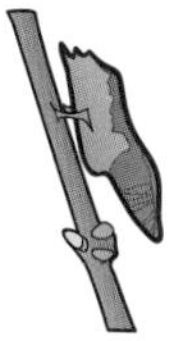  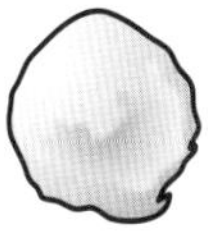

a cocoon. A cocoon looks like a long, gray cottonball. After the

 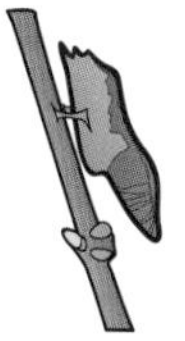

caterpillar has been in the cocoon for a few weeks, an adult

butterfly comes out of the cocoon. Butterflies are beautiful. To

become a beautiful butterfly, the insect egg must go through

many changes.

Before it becomes a butterfly, the insect goes through changes.

UNIT TWO

Values and Decision Making

The Outsiders

By S. E. Hinton

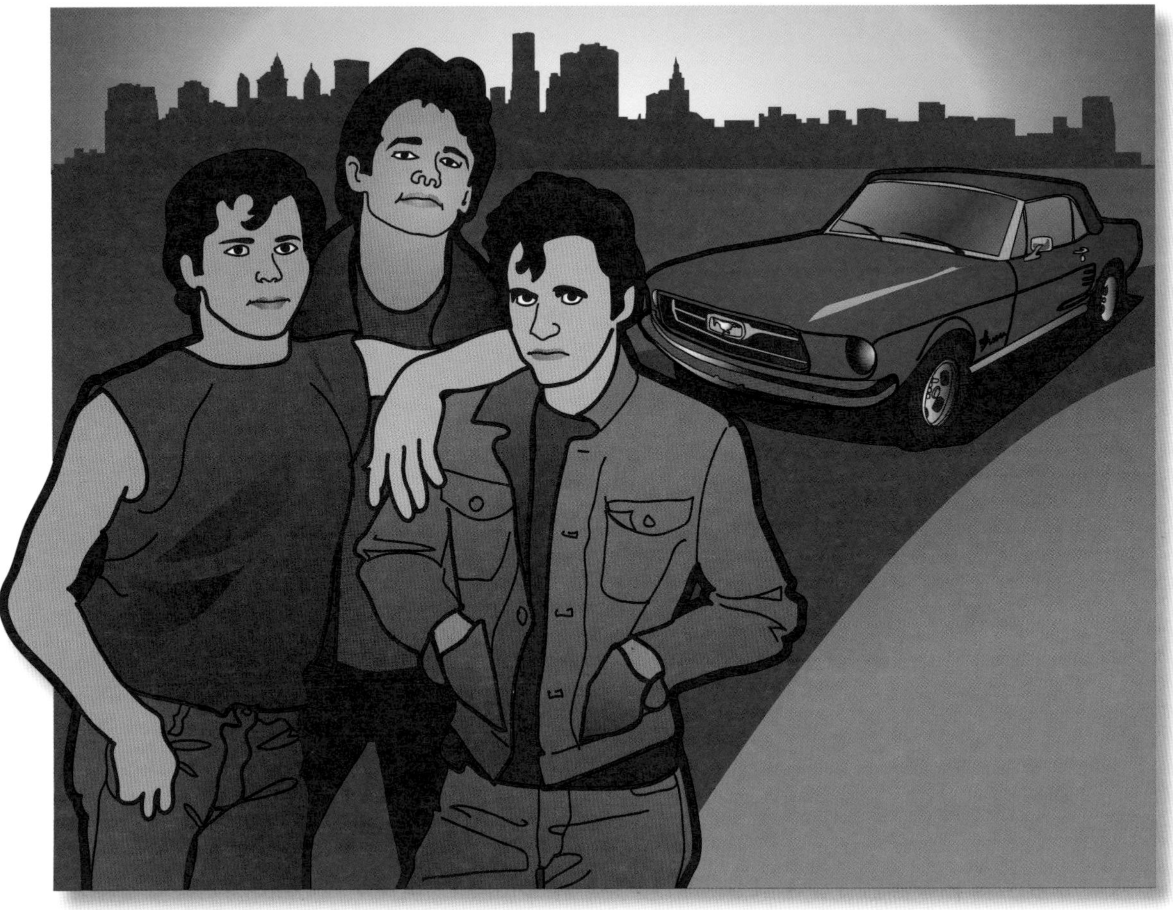

Based on the book *The Outsiders,* by S. E. Hinton

CONTENTS

CHAPTER

CHAPTER 1

Ponyboy the Greaser

 3 

Ponyboy was the youngest of three boys. His oldest brother,

 2

Darry, was 20. Darry was responsible for the care of his two

younger brothers ever since his parents died. Soda, Ponyboy's

 3 

other brother, was almost 17. The three boys hung out with

4  

four other kids. They were a tight group. They looked out for

each other. The group was kind of tough. They were called

Greasers. They lived on the poor side of town.

Ponyboy is a Greaser.

Johnny, Two-Bit, and Dally were also Greasers. One night Johnny,

Ponyboy, Dally, and Two-Bit went to a drive-in theater. They sat

 2

in front of the parked cars, and that's where they met two

girls. Dally tried to play tough guy, but that offended the girls.

Johnny was annoyed with Dally. He told Dally to leave the girls

alone. Dally left the drive-in theater.

Ponyboy is a Greaser.

CHAPTER 2

Two Girls at the Drive-in

The girls invited Ponyboy and Johnny to sit with them. The

boys soon found out the girls were Socs. The Socs were

another group of kids. They lived on the other side of town.

One girl's name was Cherry. Ponyboy and Cherry went to the

concession stand to get popcorn and cokes.

Ponyboy is a Greaser.

Ponyboy told Cherry about the time he was jumped by a

group of Socs. One evening, Ponyboy was walking home from

a movie when a bunch of boys jumped him. The boys were

Socs from the other side of town. They were different than

Greasers. Their parents had money. The Socs held Ponyboy

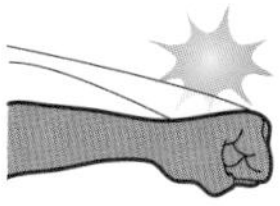   

down and hit him. Darry, Soda, and the Greasers arrived and

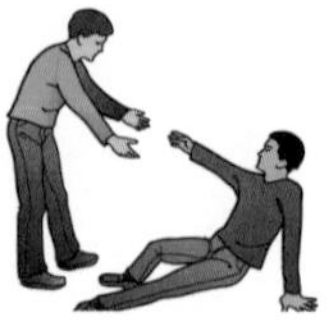

chased the Socs off. Ponyboy was happy they came to help

him. Cherry told Ponyboy not all Socs were the same, just like

Greasers were not all like Dally.

Ponyboy is a Greaser.

CHAPTER 3

The Blue Mustang

The guys decided to take the girls home. Just then, a blue

Mustang drove by. The girls hoped the Socs would not

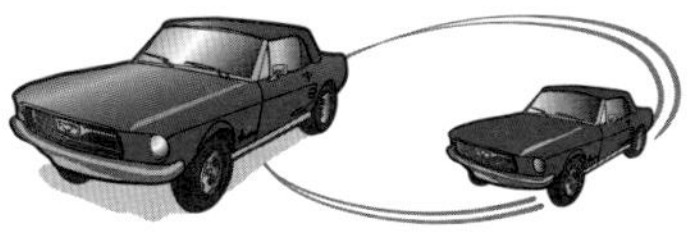

recognize them, but the blue Mustang circled around again.

This time it stopped and the boys in the Mustang tried

to start a fight. The girls got in the blue Mustang to stop

the boys from fighting.

The boys felt like outsiders.

Johnny and Ponyboy hung out at the empty lot. Ponyboy

started thinking what it would be like if his parents were still

alive. The two boys fell asleep. Ponyboy was supposed to be

home by midnight. He did not get home until 2:00 a.m.

The boys felt like outsiders.

Darry was mad at Ponyboy. He was tired of his excuses for

 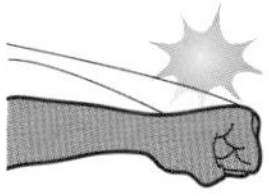 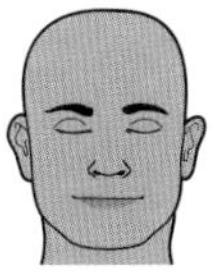

being late. Darry hit Ponyboy in the face. Ponyboy took off

and planned to run away with Johnny. But then he decided

to go back home that night. He wanted to be safe and

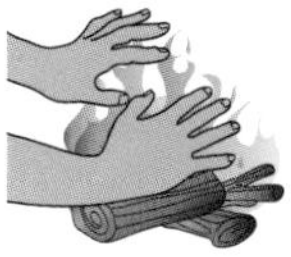 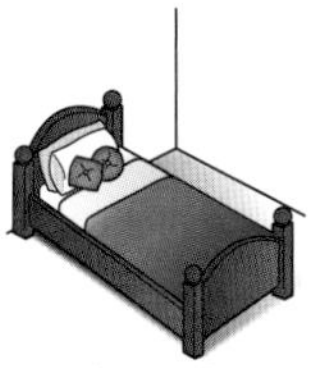

warm in his own bed.

The boys felt like outsiders.

CHAPTER 4

A Soc Dies

Ponyboy decided to hang out with Johnny for a while

to calm down before going back home. They went to the

 2  

empty lot to hang out. Then, two Socs in the blue Mustang

1  

pulled up. One of them tried to drown Ponyboy in the

 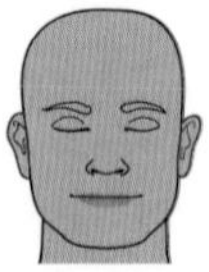  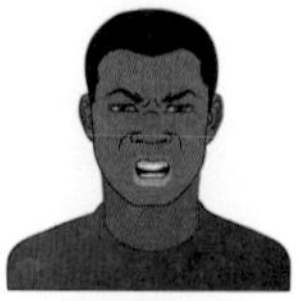

fountain. He held his head under water. Johnny got angry

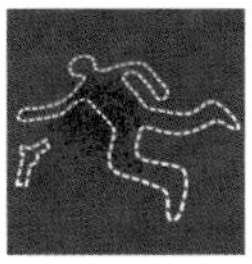 

and accidentally killed the other boy.

The boys felt like outsiders.

2  

The two boys realized they needed to get out of town fast.

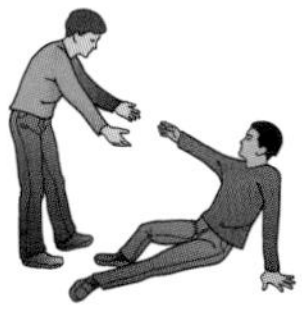  

They needed help. They went to see Dally. He told them to

take the train to Windrixville and hide in the old church on

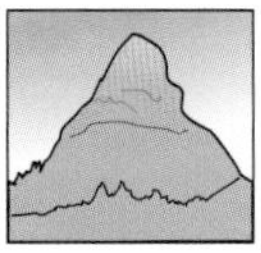   

Jay Mountain. Johnny and Ponyboy found the church. Right away,

  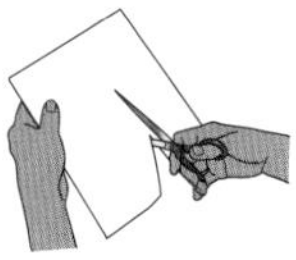 

Johnny went to the store. When he got back, he cut Ponyboy's

hair and dyed it with peroxide. Ponyboy cut Johnny's hair.

They knew their names were in the newspaper. They did not

want to get caught.

The boys felt like outsiders.

In town, Johnny bought a book, *Gone with the Wind.* He

knew Ponyboy wanted to read it. He knew they would have

a lot of time to waste because they had to stay hidden.

5

After five days, Dally arrived. He took them to Dairy Queen

to get something to eat.

The boys felt like outsiders.

CHAPTER 5

Ponyboy and Johnny Save the Kids

3

The three Greasers ate together. Johnny decided to turn himself

in to the police. He didn't want to hide from them. He did

not want Ponyboy to hide from the police either, so they

went back to the church to get their stuff. They saw the

church burning. Johnny and Ponyboy felt like it was their fault.

And kids were trapped inside the church. Ponyboy and Johnny

climbed into the church window. They wanted to save the kids.

  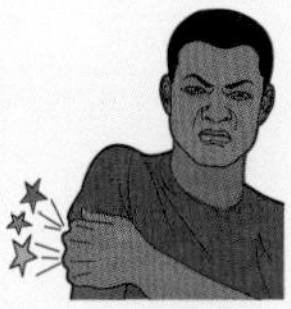

Johnny is a hero, but he got hurt.

They got all of the kids out. Thanks to the Greasers, the

kids were saved. Ponyboy then jumped out of a window. Dally

  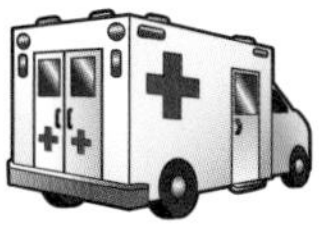

rescued Johnny. All three boys ended up in the emergency

room. Soda and Darry came to see Ponyboy. Ponyboy realized

that Darry really did love him.

Johnny is a hero, but he got hurt.

CHAPTER 6

Johnny Is Sick

  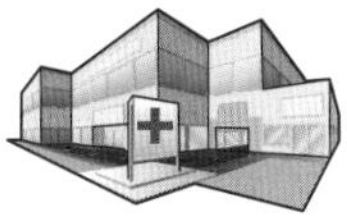

Reporters and police crowded the waiting room of the hospital.

They wanted to talk with the heroes. After several hours, they

all left and the waiting room was very quiet. The nurse finally

told the boys to go home. She told them to rest up, but

  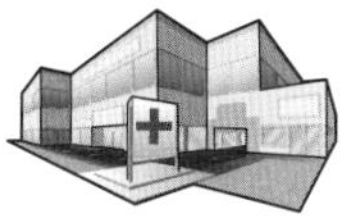

Johnny and Dally had to stay in the hospital.

Johnny is a hero, but he got hurt.

The next morning Ponyboy was the first one up. After Darry

and Soda left for work, Ponyboy cleaned the house. He wanted

it to look clean. He was afraid that child services might visit.

Now, they knew that three boys were living together without

parents. And Soda and Ponyboy were minors. Then Ponyboy went

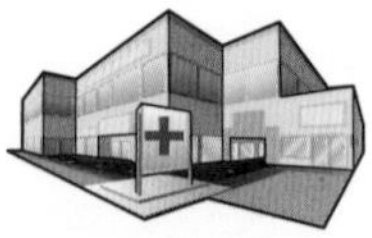  

to the hospital to visit Johnny and Dally.

Johnny is a hero, but he got hurt.

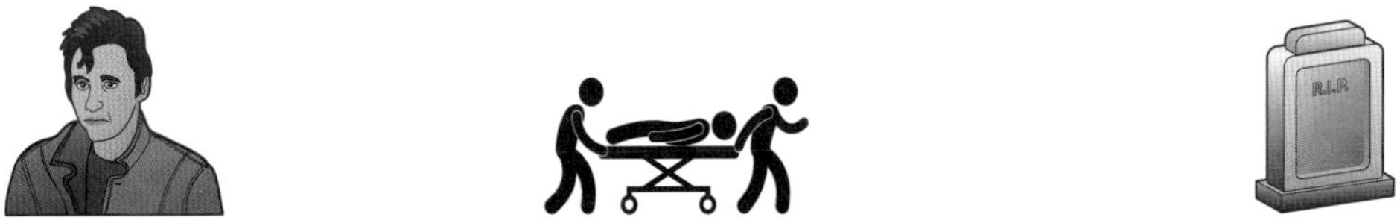

Johnny was in critical condition and might die. He was very

weak. He knew that he was paralyzed from the waist down.

He talked to the boys. Johnny's mother wanted to visit, but

Johnny refused to see her. He did not want her to see him

in critical condition. Then, he passed out. Dally was in better

condition than Johnny. He wanted to fight in the rumble that

night. Rumbles are big fights with lots of people. On the way

home, Ponyboy ran into Cherry. Ponyboy and Cherry talked

about Johnny.

Johnny is a hero, but he got hurt.

CHAPTER 7

The Greasers Win

When Ponyboy got home, the whole gang was there. He had

just enough time to eat and wash up before the rumble.

Ponyboy knew that it was wrong to fight. He thought he

needed to fight because he was part of a group that stuck

together. He was a Greaser.

Ponyboy fought in the rumble and Johnny died.

  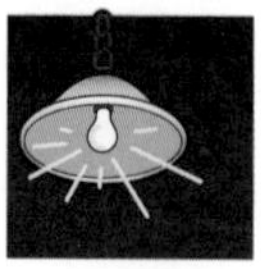

They arrived at the empty lot first. Darry stepped into the light

 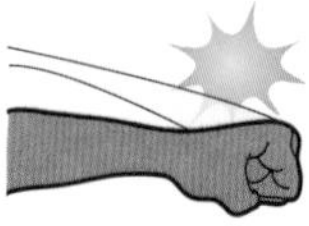 

from the lamp post. A Soc took the first swing and the fight

was on. Everyone fought hard, but the Socs soon gave up and

ran away. The Greasers won.

Ponyboy fought in the rumble and Johnny died.

They all raced to the hospital to tell Johnny. Johnny was not

good. He was dying. He told the gang that fighting was stupid.

He told Ponyboy to stay golden and to not get into any more

trouble. Ponyboy was different from the rest of the Greasers.

Johnny was proud to hear he was a hero. Then Johnny died.

Ponyboy fought in the rumble and Johnny died.

CHAPTER 8

The Hero Dies

Ponyboy walked home. He needed time to think about

everything that had happened. He was hurt badly from the

fight. He could not believe his best friend was dead. Ponyboy

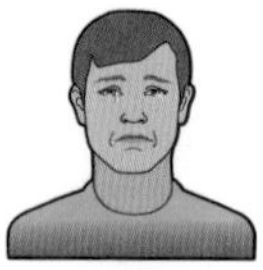  

was so sad. When he got home, he saw everyone hanging out.

All of a sudden, Ponyboy passed out. When he finally woke up,

  3

Darry told him he had been asleep for three days.

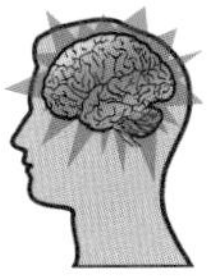 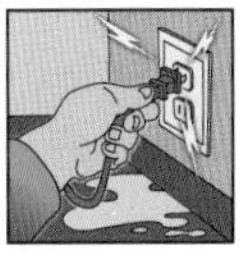

He had a concussion and he was in shock. He was delirious

and very sick. But now he was safe at home with people

who loved him.

Ponyboy fought in the rumble and Johnny died.

CHAPTER 9

Ponyboy Gets Sick

 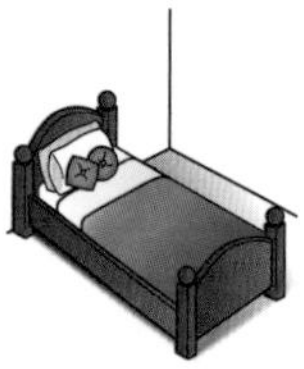 

Ponyboy was still in bed. He was very sick. Some of his

friends from school came to visit Ponyboy at his house. Randy

was one of the guys in the blue Mustang. Randy was there

the night Johnny killed a Soc. Even though he was a Soc, he

did not like fighting. He did not fight in the rumble.

 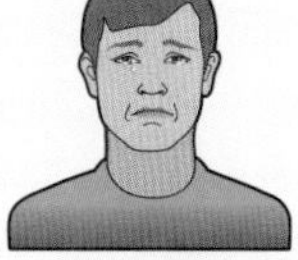 

Ponyboy was sad and wrote a story.

Randy came by to talk to Ponyboy about going to court the

next day. Randy told Ponyboy he did not have anything to

worry about because Ponyboy did not kill Bob. Johnny killed

Bob and Johnny was dead. Ponyboy was still confused from

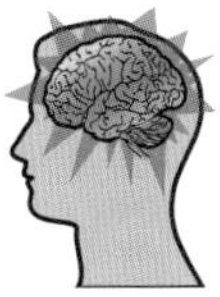  

his concussion. Ponyboy said he did not want Johnny to die

and that he should have killed the Soc instead. Ponyboy said

this because he wanted Johnny to still be alive. This was very

confusing for Randy.

 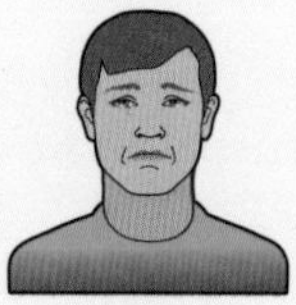 

Ponyboy was sad and wrote a story.

CHAPTER 10

Ponyboy Writes a Story

Then, Ponyboy became absent-minded. He was consumed by the

death of his best friend, Johnny, and also Bob. He was in

a daze while he grieved. He was failing in school. His only

security was his brothers. One night, he and Darry got into

another fight. He was yelling at Darry. Soda saw them fighting

and ran off.

 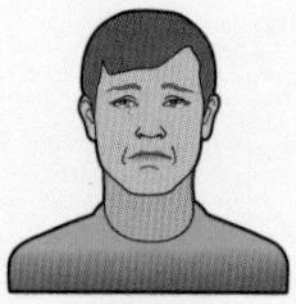 

Ponyboy was sad and wrote a story.

   3

Ponyboy and Darry finally caught up with Soda. The three

brothers took the time to talk. They realized they only had

each other. Ponyboy was trying to think of something to

write for his final English assignment. He picked up the book,

  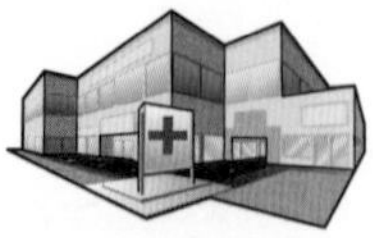

Gone with the Wind, that Johnny left for him at the hospital.

There was a note in it from Johnny. After reading it, Ponyboy

realized he needed to accept the death of his friend. He

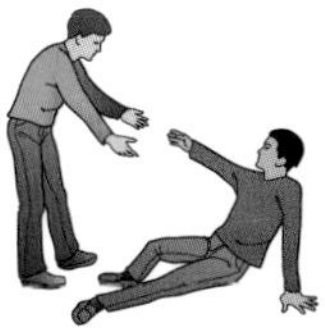  

needed to help other young boys. Ponyboy wrote his story

for his English assignment.

 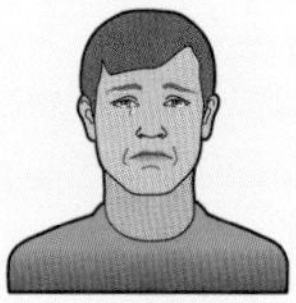 

Ponyboy was sad and wrote a story.

Neighbors

By John Sherrill

Based on the condensed story "Neighbors," by John Sherrill.

 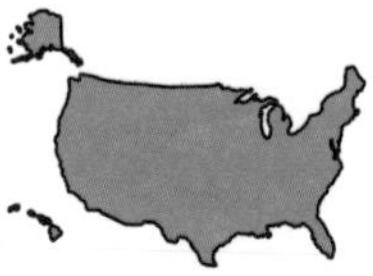 

Jiro Ninomiya came to the United States from Japan in 1900.

He bought some land near San Francisco, where he built a

house and a greenhouse for his family. On this land, he grew

roses in his greenhouse. He sold the roses in the city. He lived

across the street from a man named Frederick Aebi. Frederick

also grew roses and sold them in the city. Both men were

successful selling their roses. Years later, their sons, Tamaki and

Francis, took over their businesses. Everyone worked hard and

enjoyed each other's cultures.

The families were neighbors.

On December 7, 1941, Japan attacked Pearl Harbor. Pearl Harbor

is in the state of Hawaii. People started hearing stories that

Japanese-Americans were going to be sent away to camps in

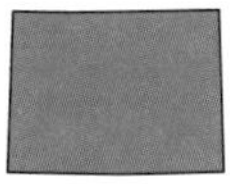   

Colorado. People who were sent to these camps could not leave.

The camps were not fun places to live. Tamaki was Japanese
 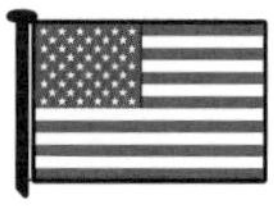 
but his wife was American. Still, he would be sent away. His

neighbor, Francis, went over to Tamaki's house and said, "I will

look after your greenhouse if you are sent away." In February of

1942, a black car came to take Tamaki and his family away to
 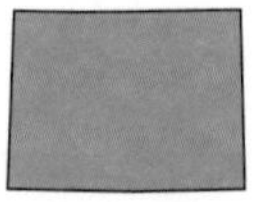
the camp in Colorado.

The families were neighbors.

Because of the war, Francis had to pull up the rosebushes and

plant vegetables in both greenhouses. He planted tomatoes in his

greenhouse and cucumbers in Tamaki's greenhouse. He grew those

vegetables and sold them in the city. Francis saved the money

from the cucumbers for Tamaki. Francis and his family worked in

their greenhouse. They worked in Tamaki's greenhouse, too. The

children were responsible. They worked before they went to

  3

school. Francis worked 16 hours a day for three years.

The families were neighbors.

The war ended and Tamaki's family came home. Francis came

to pick them up at the train station. He drove them to their

house. Their greenhouse was clean and the vegetables were

healthy. Francis gave Tamaki the money he had saved from

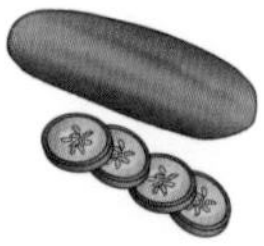  

selling the cucumbers. Tamaki was thankful.

Today, Tamaki's family still lives across the street from Francis's

family. Both families are growing roses again and selling them in

the city. They share happy times like graduations and weddings.

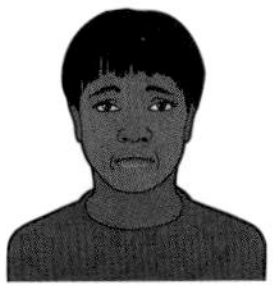 

They share sad times like funerals.

The families were neighbors.

Dreams

By Langston Hughes

Hold fast to dreams

For if dreams die

Life is a broken-winged bird

That cannot fly.

Hold fast to dreams

For when dreams go

Life is a barren field

Frozen with snow.

Gandhi

Mahatma Gandhi was born in India in 1869. He was a lawyer.

He helped his country in its struggle for civil rights. Civil rights

are the rights and privileges all people in a country have.

Gandhi did not believe in fighting.

He used peaceful ways to solve problems.

India was ruled by Great Britain. The people of India were

unhappy about that. They felt British law was unfair to Indian

people. They wanted to rule their own country. In 1921, Gandhi

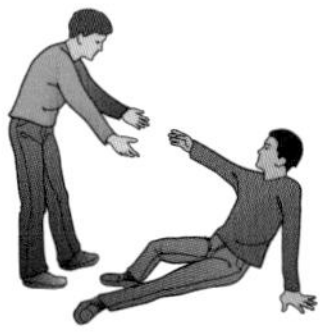  

fought to help the people of India work with their government.

He wanted to find a peaceful way to resolve conflicts. Then, in

1921, Gandhi became the leader of India.

Gandhi did not believe in fighting.

 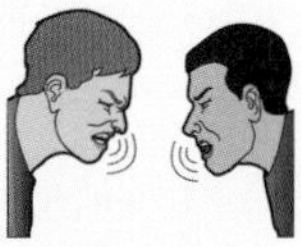

He used peaceful ways to solve problems.

  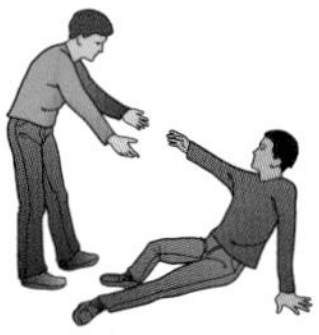

When Gandhi became the leader of India, he helped the

country write new laws. He asked the people of India not to

fight Britain, but to refuse to buy or use their products. The

 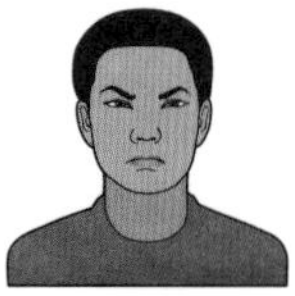  

British government was angry with Gandhi, and they sent him

 2

to jail for two years.

Gandhi did not believe in fighting.

 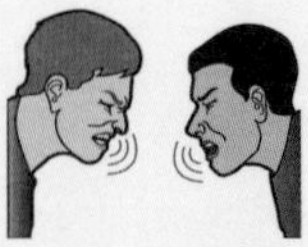

He used peaceful ways to solve problems.

  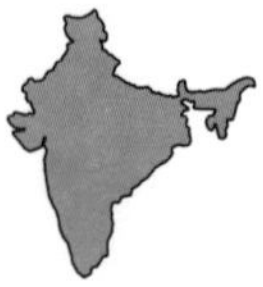

After jail, Gandhi again organized the people of India to

peacefully protest British rule. India's people refused to buy or

use products from Britain. Instead, they marched peacefully to

protest the British government. Even though the people of India

 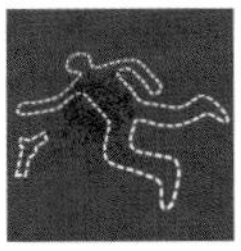 

did not fight, many were killed or sent to prison. In 1947,

India was granted independence from Britain.

Gandhi did not believe in fighting.

 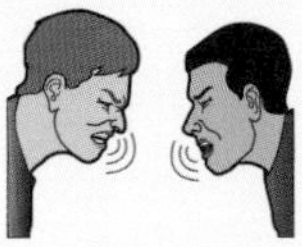

He used peaceful ways to solve problems.

In 1948, Gandhi was shot and killed. Many around the world

were sad to hear that. Gandhi helped to influence Martin Luther

King, Jr. and Nelson Mandela. Both used Gandhi's peaceful ways

to lead their own civil rights movements. Gandhi is a hero.

Gandhi did not believe in fighting.

 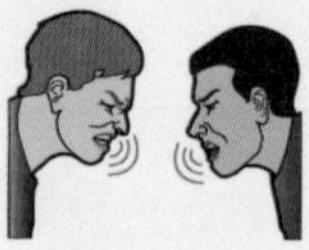

He used peaceful ways to solve problems.